My Reptile Hospital

Written by **Frank Christianson**

Illustrated by **Wayne Andreason**

Welcome to my reptile hospital!
You're just in time to help me
visit my patients.

The first floor of my hospital is a swamp.
I get my bag and walk to a murky, green pond.
There, a family of alligators with head colds
is sneezing and sniffling.

It takes a steady hand
to take the temperature
of this baby alligator.
I have to be careful
around these patients.
They are among the world's largest reptiles,
and those sharp teeth are dangerous.
But I'm not afraid.
I know these alligators
would rather eat fish
than a herpetologist—that's me,
a person who studies reptiles!

The second floor of my hospital
is a dense, green rain forest.
I walk under a huge kapok tree
and find my patient—
or at least part of my patient.
One long coil of a 30-foot python
hangs down sadly.

Poor python.

Her breakfast didn't go down right.

Now she has a stomachache.

For a snake that can swallow

whole goats and pigs,

that can be a problem.

I watch out for her coils

as I feed her some pills.

I don't want to get hugged too hard!

I almost pass by my next patient,
a small, green chameleon
waiting on a leafy branch.
The chameleon is hard to see
because his color blends with the leaves.
A chameleon can change his color.
He can't copy every color in the rainbow.
But he blends very well into his jungle home.

This chameleon has a problem.
One of his large eyes,
which can move in any direction,
has something caught in it.
I wash out the eye
and send the chameleon on his way
to hunt more insects.

The top floor of my hospital
is a dry, rocky desert.
My patient there is easy to find.
His skin looks like a beautiful, beaded belt.
But nothing else is beautiful
about the gila monster.
He is mean and cranky
with a poisonous bite.
I check the bandage on his tail
very carefully.
Then I wave good-bye.

For my last stop,
I go out the back door
to a sandy seaside beach.
There a giant sea turtle rests
in the shallows.
Every year she swims
thousands of miles
through warm ocean waters
to this very beach.

This turtle isn't sick.
She just needs a place to lay her eggs.
I find her a nice spot above the tide line
where the eggs will be safe and warm.
She follows me slowly,
pushing herself along with her strong flippers.

I leave the sea turtle
digging a hole in the sand
and go back to my office
for a cold drink.
Sometimes the hospital gets too hot,
even for me,
but that's how these cold-blooded
reptiles like it.